Unputdownable Reading tests from CGP!

This CGP book is packed with short, sharp reading tests
for KS2 English — it's a brilliant way to help pupils
prepare for the SATS Reading Test.

We've made sure the tests are just like mini versions of the real
SATS, including reading texts that become progressively
more challenging throughout each set.

But wait, there's more — enjoyable puzzle pages,
full answers and even handy scoresheets. Excellent!

What CGP is all about

Our sole aim here at CGP is to produce the highest quality books
— carefully written, immaculately presented and
dangerously close to being funny.

Then we work our socks off to get them out to you
— at the cheapest possible prices.

Contents

Set A

Test 1 2

Test 2 5

Test 3 8

Test 4 11

Test 5 14

Test 6 17

Puzzle 20

Scoresheet 21

Set B

Test 1 22

Test 2 25

Test 3 28

Test 4 31

Test 5 34

Test 6 37

Puzzle 40

Scoresheet 41

Set C

Test 1 42

Test 2 45

Test 3 48

Test 4 51

Test 5 54

Test 6 57

Puzzle 60

Scoresheet 61

Answers 62

Progress Chart 70

Published by CGP

Editors: Emma Bonney, Emma Crighton, Lucy Loveluck, Heather McClelland, Sabrina Robinson, Louise Taylor
With thanks to David Broadbent and Rebecca Tate for the proofreading.
With thanks to Jan Greenway and Laura Jakubowski for the copyright research.

With thanks to iStock.com for permission to use the images on page 31.

National Curriculum references throughout answers reproduced under the terms of the Open Government
Licence. http://www.nationalarchives.gov.uk/doc/open-government-licence/version/3/

ISBN: 978 1 78294 239 9
Clipart from Corel®
Printed by Bell & Bain Ltd, Glasgow.
Based on the classic CGP style created by Richard Parsons.

A Walk in the Park

Isha slumped back on her sofa and found herself getting more and more annoyed. Her living room was too hot and too boring, and she couldn't bear to stay cooped up any longer. She sprang to her feet and decided that she had to go outside for some fresh air. Maybe her neighbour Georgia would want to play.

"Mum," she called, "can I go outside and play with Georgia?"

"Absolutely not!" her mum replied. "Even though it looks nice now, it's going to rain later and I don't want you to get wet."

Despite her mum's warning, Isha was determined to escape the living room. Her mum had gone upstairs to do some work in her office, so Isha thought she could make a break for it without her noticing. She slipped her phone from her pocket and quietly called Georgia as she snuck out of the house.

The girls met in the street and chatted happily as they wandered through their neighbourhood. Before long, Isha wondered if they had got lost — they were in a small park she didn't recognise, and none of the buildings or street names nearby looked familiar. However, Isha soon felt even more concerned as some heavy clouds rolled in. The first raindrops fell, and the girls decided to head home. Isha threw her jacket over her head to shelter from the rain and hoped that Georgia knew her way back.

Isha's heart was pounding as she tried to sneak back into the house without her mum noticing. However, to Isha's surprise, her mum was waiting patiently in the living room for her.

"Come on," said her mum, "let's get you into some dry clothes before you catch a cold."

1. What **two** things irritated Isha about her living room?

    1)...

    2)...

    2 marks

2. Why did Isha's mum tell her not to go outside?

    ....

    1 mark

3. *they wandered through their neighbourhood*
    What does the word *wandered* mean in this sentence?

    Tick **one** box.

smiled	☐
strolled	☐
talked	☐
ran	☐

    1 mark

4. *Isha's heart was pounding as she tried to sneak back into the house*
    What does this tell you about how Isha was feeling?

    ....

    ....

    1 mark

5.   Do you think Isha had been to that park before?

Yes ☐   No ☐

Use the text to give reasons for your answer.

....

....

....

....

....

....

....

3 marks

END OF TEST

/ 8

There are **6 questions** in this test.
Give yourself **10 minutes** to read the text and answer the questions.

Making Rainbows

In 1666, Isaac Newton was the first person to discover that white light can be split up into different colours.

He shone the light from a window through an optical prism — a piece of glass with triangular sides. The result was a pattern of colours called a spectrum: red, orange, yellow, green, blue, indigo and violet. This is the same pattern of colours that makes up a rainbow.

Newton then carried out more experiments and found that all these colours could be put together to make white light again.

Testing Newton's discovery

You can test the fact that the colours of the spectrum combine to make white for yourself, at home or at school. Just follow these simple steps:

1. Using a pair of compasses, draw a circle with a diameter of 10 centimetres on a piece of white card (any thickness will do).

2. Use a protractor to divide it into 7 sections, each about 51 degrees wide.

3. Use crayons to colour them in the colours of the spectrum (as in diagram A). Cut out the circle with a pair of scissors.

4. Make a small hole through the centre and push a pencil through.

5. Spin the disc and see what happens.
   The colours should combine to make a whitish colour (diagram B).

Diagram A    Diagram B

1. According to the text, what did Isaac Newton discover in 1666?
    Tick **one** box.

    The combination of colours that make up a rainbow ☐

    That you can split white light into seven different colours ☐

    That an optical prism has triangular sides ☐

    That you can make white light using a circle of card ☐

    _____
    1 mark

2. *the same pattern of colours that makes up a rainbow*
    Explain how comparing the spectrum to a rainbow helps the reader
    to imagine what the spectrum looks like.

    ....

    ....
    _____
    1 mark

3. Write the numbers 1 to 5 in the boxes to put these instructions from
    the text into the right order. The first one has been done for you.

    Make a hole in the middle, then put a pencil in the hole. ☐

    Split it into seven sections. ☐

    Colour in and cut out the circle. ☐

    Draw a circle. ☐ 1

    Spin the disc on the table. ☐
    _____
    1 mark

4. The text says you will need a pencil to follow these instructions. List **three** other pieces of equipment you will need.

1)...

2)...

3)...

1 mark

5. How does the second half of the text make it sound easy to test Newton's discovery? Give **two** ways.

1)...

2)...

2 marks

6. Complete this table about the second half of the text.

How wide does each section of the circle need to be?	
What should the diameter of the circle be?	
Which two colours should be next to blue on the circle?	

2 marks

END OF TEST

/ 8

There are **6 questions** in this test.
Give yourself **10 minutes** to read the text and answer the questions.

Bungee Jumping

Definition

Bungee jumping is the sport of leaping from a high structure while attached to a stretchy cord. The cord is called a bungee: it is attached to the person's ankles at one end and the structure they're jumping off at the other. The bungee is just long enough to allow the jumper to spring back just above the ground without touching it. The cord springs the jumper back up into the air several times – making them look like a human yo-yo! When it does finally stop, the jumper then has to wait to be lowered safely to the ground.

Famous Jump Sites

Bungee jumps are performed from sites all over the world, including from cranes, bridges, dams and even hot-air balloons. The Verzasca Dam in Switzerland is one of the highest permanent jumping sites in the world, with jumpers plunging approximately 220m.

The Kawarau Bridge jump in New Zealand is only 43m high, but thousands of people flock to this jumping site since this is where commercial bungee jumping first began. Tandem jumps take place here too; couples can plunge together towards the turquoise river below.

One of the world's most famous jumps is from the Victoria Falls Bridge in Zambia. Not only is there the thrill of jumping, but with the largest waterfalls on Earth behind and the Zambezi River below, it is a truly spectacular experience.

Risks

Bungee jumping is considered to be a dangerous sport by some people, and there have been fatalities. Most injuries occur when the bungee isn't attached to the jump platform or the jumper properly. However, it's quite rare for things to go wrong, and most jumpers say the experience is thrilling, with many admitting they would do it again!

---

1.   What is a bungee attached to? Mention **two** things.

      1)...

      2)...   _____

                                                                        1 mark

2.   Why do so many people choose to bungee jump off the
      Kawarau Bridge in New Zealand?

      ....

      ....   _____
                                                                                              1 mark

3.   Circle the correct option.
      The Victoria Falls Bridge is in:

      (**Zambezi.**)   (**Switzerland.**)   (**Zambia.**)   (**New Zealand.**)   _____
                                                                                              1 mark

4.   **Find** and **copy** two words from the fourth paragraph that suggest
      that bungee jumping from the Victoria Falls bridge is an exciting
      experience.

      1)...

      2)...   _____
                                                                                              1 mark

5. Read each statement and **tick** whether it is fact or opinion.

	Fact	**Opinion**
People bungee jump from cranes.	☐	☐
The Verzasca Dam is one of the highest permanent jumping sites in the world.	☐	☐
Bungee jumping is thrilling.	☐	☐

1 mark

6. Write down how a person might feel when they are about to do a bungee jump. Give reasons from the text to support your answer.

....

....

....

....

....

....

....

3 marks

END OF TEST

/ 8

There are **6 questions** in this test.
Give yourself **10 minutes** to read the text and answer the questions.

Challenging Captivity

Skedingdale Zoo has announced that it will be acquiring a wild female elephant called Nia. The letter below is a response to the announcement.

Lower Wood Cottage
Skedingdale
SKE B3R

Skedingdale Zoo
Skedingdale
SKE B0R

2nd September 2014

Dear Sir or Madam,

I am writing in response to the news that your zoo intends to acquire a wild elephant. I am disgusted to learn that you intend to keep a wild animal prisoner, and I do not believe this to be a cause for celebration. Captivity is a crime, and I am appalled by your actions.

As I am sure you are aware, elephants roam across large expanses of land. By housing Nia in an enclosure, you are sentencing her to an unhappy existence. She will pace up and down the boundaries of her confined patch of earth, longing for the open plains of her homeland with sadness in her eyes.

How would you feel if the walls of your house were replaced by thick, black, solid bars, through which passers-by could poke their nosy little heads to gawp at you? This will be Nia's fate if you execute your plans and force her to leave her family in Africa — just so Skedingdale Zoo can fulfil its own selfish desire to possess an exotic animal.

I beg you to leave Nia where she is. It is not too late.

Yours faithfully,
Mr Clarke

1. In what month did Mr Clarke write his letter?

   .... _____

1 mark

2. What does the word *disgusted* tell us about how Mr Clarke feels?

   .... _____

1 mark

3. According to the text, what is the difference between an elephant's life in captivity and in the wild?

   ....

   .... _____

1 mark

4. Where does Nia's family live?

   .... _____

1 mark

5. Which of these sentences best summarises Mr Clarke's message for the zoo? **Tick** the correct option.

Free Nia the elephant. ☐

Leave Nia in Africa. ☐

Nia would be safer in the zoo. ☐

Free all zoo animals. ☐

_____
1 mark

6. How do you think Mr Clarke would feel about using elephants in the circus? Use the text to support your answer.

....

....

....

....

....

....

....

_____
3 marks

END OF TEST

| / 8 |

Set A: Test 5

There are **6 questions** in this test.
Give yourself **10 minutes** to read the text and answer the questions.

An Adaptation of 'The Sea' by Barry Cornwall

The sea! the sea! the open sea!
The blue, the fresh, the ever free!
Without a mark, without a bound,
It runneth the earth's wide regions round;
5   It plays with the clouds; it mocks the skies;
Or like a cradled creature lies.

I'm on the sea! I'm on the sea!
I am where I would ever be;
With the blue above, and the blue below,
10   And silence wheresoe'er I go.
If a storm should come and awake the deep,
What matter? I shall ride and sleep.

I love, O, how I love to ride
On the fierce, foaming, bursting tide,
15   When every mad wave drowns the moon
Or whistles aloft his tempest tune,
And tells how goeth the world below,
And why the sou'west blasts do blow.

I never was on the dull, tame shore,
20   But I lov'd the great sea more and more,
And backwards flew to her billowy breast,
Like a bird that seeketh its mother's nest;
And a mother she was, and is, to me;
For I was born on the open sea!

25   I've liv'd, since then, in calm and strife,
Full fifty summers, a sailor's life,
With wealth to spend and a power to range,
But never have sought nor sighed for change;
And Death, whenever he comes to me,
30   Shall come on the wild, unbounded sea!

1. *With the blue above, and the blue below*
   What **two** things does the word *blue* refer to in this line?

   1)...

   2)...

2. Which animal is the narrator compared to?

   ....

3. Where does the narrator say they were born?
   Tick **one** box.

   In a bird's nest ☐

   On the land ☐

   At sea ☐

   In the south west ☐

4. *I've liv'd, since then, in calm and strife,*
   What does the word *strife* mean in this line? Tick **one** box.

   Conflict ☐

   Happiness ☐

   Storms ☐

   Sadness ☐

5. How old is the narrator?

.... _____

6. One of the main ideas in this poem is that the sea is a living thing. Using evidence from the text, explain **two** ways the poet suggests this.

....

....

....

....

....

....

.... _____

3 marks

END OF TEST

/ 8

Set A: Test 6

There are **7 questions** in this test.
Give yourself **10 minutes** to read the text and answer the questions.

An Extract from 'The War of the Worlds' by H.G. Wells

A spacecraft from Mars has crash-landed on Earth, creating a massive crater near the town of Woking. People have gathered around the edge of the pit to look at the Martians and their craft.

After the glimpse I had had of the Martians emerging from the cylinder in which they had come to the Earth from their planet, a kind of fascination paralysed my actions. I remained standing knee-deep in the heather, staring at the mound that hid them. I was a battleground of fear and curiosity.

I did not dare to go back towards the pit, but I felt a passionate longing to peer into it. I began walking, therefore, in a big curve, seeking some point of vantage and continually looking at the sand heaps that hid these new-comers to our Earth. Once a leash of thin black whips, like the arms of an octopus, flashed across the sunset and was immediately withdrawn, and afterwards a thin rod rose up, joint by joint, bearing at its apex a circular disk that spun with a wobbling motion. What could be going on there?

Most of the spectators had gathered in one or two groups — one a little crowd towards Woking, the other a knot of people in the direction of Chobham. Evidently they shared my mental conflict. There were few near me. One man I approached — he was, I perceived, a neighbour of mine, though I did not know his name — and accosted. But it was scarcely a time for articulate conversation.

"What ugly brutes!" he said. "Good God! What ugly brutes!" He repeated this over and over again.

"Did you see a man in the pit?" I said; but he made no answer to that. We became silent, and stood watching for a time side by side, deriving, I fancy, a certain comfort in one another's company. Then I shifted my position to a little knoll that gave me the advantage of a yard or more of elevation and when I looked for him presently he was walking towards Woking.

 Set A: Test 6

1. Circle the correct option.
    The vehicle the Martians arrive in is in the shape of a:

    Cylinder   **Circle**   **Mound**   **Planet**

    _____
    1 mark

2. **Find** and **copy** a word which tells us that the narrator cannot move.

    ....
    _____
    1 mark

3. What time of day is it in the extract?

    ....
    _____
    1 mark

4. Look at the paragraph beginning _I did not dare to go back..._
    Find and **copy** a word or phrase from this paragraph which tells us
    that the narrator is curious.

    ....

    ....
    _____
    1 mark

5. _One man I approached — he was, I perceived, a neighbour of
    mine..._
    What does the word _perceived_ mean in this sentence?

    ....
    _____
    1 mark

6. Write the numbers 1 to 5 in the boxes to put these events from the text into the right order. The first one has been done for you.

The narrator speaks to his neighbour. ☐

A rod rises up out of the spacecraft. ☐

The neighbour is seen heading towards Woking. ☐

The narrator sees the Martians emerge. 1

The narrator climbs a small hill to get a better view. ☐

_____
1 mark

7. How does this extract show that the spacecraft's crash-landing is an unusual event?
Mention **two** things from the text.

....

....

....

....

....
_____
2 marks

END OF TEST

/ 8

This puzzle is a brilliant way to practise your word-making skills.

Haunted House

Kayin is exploring a haunted house, but it is falling down. Use the bricks below to repair the walls, so they form words that mean **to make someone afraid**. Each brick can only be used once. The remaining bricks can be used to spell out the scariest thing that Kayin finds in the haunted house. One word has been done for you.

The scariest thing in the house is a ☐ ☐ ☐.

You've finished a full set of tests — well done!

Now it's time to put your scores in here
and see how you're getting on.

	Score	
Test 1		/8
Test 2		/8
Test 3		/8
Test 4		/8
Test 5		/8
Test 6		/8
Total		**/48**

Once you've got a score out of 48, check it out in the table below...

0 – 23	If you got a lot of questions wrong, don't worry. Ask an adult to help you work out the **areas** you need **more practice** on. Then have another go at **this** set of tests.
24 – 36	If you got half-marks or better, you're doing well. **Read** back over your **incorrect** answers and make sure you know **why** they're wrong. Then try the **next set** of tests.
37 – 48	Woohoo! Now have a go at the **next set** of tests — can you beat your score?

But before you do... bend your brain round this one:

Each word below starts and ends with the same letter. Can you complete the words?

__ i v i n __   __ o i l e __   __ a r s n i __   __ a t h t u __

There are **6 questions** in this test.
Give yourself **10 minutes** to read the text and answer the questions.

CALLING ALL ADVENTURERS!
Stuck for something to do next summer?
Look no further than Fierce Forest Holiday Camp.

What is Fierce Forest?

Fierce Forest is a summer camp that runs in the school holidays. Our fantastic woodland site is fully equipped for the ultimate summer adventure: awesome log cabins, an amazing array of activities and expert camp leaders who will look after you and teach you the ways of the wild. Additionally, everyone at Fierce Forest is a member of one of our four teams: Firecrests, Warblers, Blackcaps and Sparrowhawks. Win points for your team to earn rewards, such as an afternoon treetop exploring or extra marshmallow rations for those all-important campfire sessions.

One of our log cabins

What can I do at Fierce Forest?

The choice is yours! These are just a few of the whole host of activities we have on offer for a fun-filled fortnight with our qualified leaders:

- abseiling
- wildlife walks
- white water rafting
- wood trekking
- arts and crafts
- sports and games

Rafting down the river

We all have responsibilities around camp too, with each team taking it in turns to cook for everyone. We'll even teach you how to build the campfires! There's also plenty of time and space to just kick back and relax — this is a holiday, after all.

Fierce Forest Holiday Camp • **Suitable for ages 9-14**

---

1. **Find** and **copy** a phrase from the first paragraph which means 'the greatest summer experience'.

    .... _____

2. *an amazing array of activities*
    Which word in this phrase tells you that there is a selection of things to do at Fierce Forest Holiday Camp?

    .... _____

3. How long are holidays at Fierce Forest Holiday Camp?

    .... _____

4. What would you learn to build at Fierce Forest Holiday Camp?

    .... _____

5. Read each statement and **tick** whether it is true or false.

	True	**False**
You might be in the Kingfishers team at Fierce Forest.	☐	☐
Fierce Forest is suitable for 11-year-olds.	☐	☐
Everyone gets to go treetop exploring.	☐	☐
There are four different activities to choose from.	☐	☐

1 mark

6. Explain how the information in the text makes the Fierce Forest Holiday Camp sound attractive to both parents and children. Use evidence from the text to support your answer.

....

....

....

....

....

....

....

3 marks

END OF TEST

/ 8

There are **6 questions** in this test.
Give yourself **10 minutes** to read the text and answer the questions.

A Dream Come True

Ella Casperwell works as a chef in a busy restaurant in Norwich. Priti Malik went to talk to her.

Priti   *Hi Ella. Why did you want to become a chef?*

Ella   I've loved food for as long as I can remember. As a young girl, I helped my parents with the cooking. The trouble was that they weren't very good at it! My grandfather was the person who showed me how interesting cooking could be — he still makes the best casserole I've ever tasted. He encouraged me to try new recipes and that's when I really fell in love with cooking and decided I wanted to become a chef.

Priti   *So are you glad you followed your childhood dream?*

Ella   Of course I am! I still love cooking as much as ever. I'm passionate about using fresh ingredients and I get a lot of satisfaction from preparing food for customers at the restaurant. I must admit that I was surprised by how stressful the job can be, as well as the long hours I have to work. But, even with those drawbacks, being a chef is brilliant.

Priti   *What are your ambitions for the future?*

Ella   For the next few years I think I'll stay where I am. I want to improve enough to get promoted, and maybe even become the head chef here! One day, I'd like to work in London. I've lived in Norwich my whole life, so it would be good to live somewhere else eventually.

Priti   *Do you have any advice for anyone who wants to become a chef?*

Ella   Being a chef is absolutely amazing, but you need to put in the hours to succeed. The best chefs I know are always pushing themselves to learn more so that they stay at the top of their game.

1.　Who inspired Ella's love of cooking? Circle the correct option.

Her mum	Her head chef
Her grandfather	Priti Malik

_____
1 mark

2.　Read each statement and **tick** to show whether it is fact or opinion.

	Fact	Opinion
Ella's grandfather makes the best casserole.	☐	☐
Ella has always lived in Norwich.	☐	☐
Being a chef is always stressful.	☐	☐

_____
1 mark

3.　What does Ella find satisfying about her job?

....

....
_____
1 mark

4.　List **two** things that surprised Ella about being a chef.

1)...

2)...
_____
1 mark

5.	Ella said to Priti, *you need to put in the hours*.
	What did she mean by this phrase?

	....

	....
	

6.	What do you think Ella might do to encourage someone who
	doesn't enjoy cooking?
	Use the text to support your answer.

	....

	....

	....

	....

	....

	....

	....
	
	3 marks

END OF TEST

/ 8

There are **6 questions** in this test.
Give yourself **10 minutes** to read the text and answer the questions.

The Flight of Daedalus and Icarus

This is an old story about an inventor called Daedalus.

Daedalus had been brought by the King to the island of Crete in order to build a labyrinth — a maze filled with winding passages.
The King was so impressed with the results that he refused to let Daedalus leave.

Daedalus grew very unhappy. He would stand on the edge of the cliffs beside the King's palace, looking longingly out to sea towards his homeland.

One day, as he stood there, Daedalus noticed the birds flying over the sea to Greece. He became transfixed as they swooped and dived through the air like acrobats. "If they can fly, why can't I?" the inventor thought to himself.

Working secretly, Daedalus fashioned two pairs of wings out of feathers and wax — one pair for him, and one for his son, Icarus. He made the wings large enough to support the weight of a person, and he put straps on them, so that they could be worn on the arms. Soon, the human wings were ready.

Daedalus and Icarus donned their new limbs and stood expectantly at the edge of the cliffs. Before they took off, Daedalus warned his son: "Do not fly too close to the sun, or else the wax in your wings will melt." Then, with a brave leap, they escaped into the air and set a course for Greece.

Icarus soon grew overexcited. "Look how high I can fly!" he shouted to his father. Daedalus pleaded with his son to be careful, but, ignoring his father's warning, Icarus flew too high, and his wings melted in the bright sunlight. He tumbled down into the sea and drowned.

1.   Daedalus went to Crete to...

Tick **one** box.

learn to fly.   ☐

visit his son Icarus.   ☐

build a labyrinth.   ☐

talk to the King.   ☐

_____
1 mark

2.   Look at the sentence *Daedalus grew very unhappy.*
     Why was Daedalus unhappy?

     ....

     ....
_____
1 mark

3.   The author writes that the birds moved *like acrobats*.
     What does this suggest about the birds?

     ....

     ....
_____
1 mark

4.   What does the word *transfixed* tell you about Daedalus' reaction
     to the birds?

     ....

     ....
_____
1 mark

5.   Why did Daedalus work *secretly*?

    ....

    .... ———

6.   Using your own words, summarise what happens in the last
      two paragraphs.

    ....

    ....

    ....

    ....

    ....

    ....

    ....

    .... ———

END OF TEST

/ 8

There are **7 questions** in this test.
Give yourself **10 minutes** to read the text and answer the questions.

FUN DAY RAISES FUNDS FOR FRIEND

By Julie Wakefield

Year Six pupils at Ramsway Junior School hosted a Charity Fun Day on Saturday, donating the proceeds to the Disability Support Unit at St. Mary's Hospital.

The children's efforts began long before the day itself, as year group leader, Mr James Parkinson, explained: "One of the Year Six classes came up with the idea back in January, and since then all of the planning has been coordinated by the pupils themselves."

The Fun Day began at 10am with the children's races. Students of all ages took part in light-hearted events such as an egg and spoon race and an inflatable obstacle course, with prizes donated by local businesses.

Come lunchtime, the school field was full of local families, many enjoying picnics in the bright April sunshine.

The morning sack race was a real hit.

A wide variety of activities were on offer throughout the afternoon. One of the most entertaining was the adults three-legged race, perhaps topped only by the final 'Soak a Teacher' event at 4pm. Students could pay one pound each to aim wet sponges at a member of Ramsway's staff.

"I must say I was a little nervous about this one at first," said a rather wet Mr Parkinson, "but since it's for charity I was happy to be a part of the fun."

This particular charity has a special importance for the pupils at Ramsway, as one of their classmates, Sophia Martin, attends the Disability Support Unit once a fortnight. "I love going to St. Mary's," Sophia told the Ramsway Herald. "There are loads of fun activities, like wheelchair basketball."

"The support St. Mary's provide is invaluable," said Sophia's mother, May Martin. "It's so wonderful to see it backed by the school in this way."

Sophia has been going to St. Mary's for many years.

The Fun Day raised £1500 in total, and pupils hope to add to this with the ticket sales from their Leaver's Show in the Summer Term.

1. Read each statement and **tick** whether it is true or false.

	True	False
The Fun Day began at 9am.	☐	☐
The 'Soak a Teacher' event was at 4pm.	☐	☐
Sophia's mother is Mary Martin.	☐	☐
The Fun Day raised £1000 in total.	☐	☐

1 mark

2. In what month did the Fun Day take place?

.... _____

1 mark

3. Why is Mr Parkinson *rather wet*?

....

.... _____

1 mark

4. How often does Sophia go to the Disability Support Unit?

.... _____

1 mark

5.   What activity takes place at St. Mary's Hospital? Circle **one** option.

An obstacle course   Sack races

A picnic   Basketball

1 mark

6.   What does the word *invaluable* suggest about the support that
St. Mary's provides?

....

....

1 mark

7.   How do you think Sophia feels about her classmates raising funds
for St. Mary's? Give a reason for your answer.

....

....

....

2 marks

END OF TEST

/ 8

There are **6 questions** in this test.
Give yourself **10 minutes** to read the text and answer the questions.

Some people are worried about the impact that social media has on the lives of young people. The following text was written by a reporter who tried to find out whether social media has a positive or negative effect on children.

Is Social Media Really a Problem?

Social media websites are communities where users can share photos and talk to each other online. They are very popular — millions of people use social media every day. Although some people think social media is a positive thing, many are concerned about the negative impact it can have on young people.

Munira Karthik, a Year 6 pupil, thinks that social media has lots of benefits. "I get very nervous when I talk to people in real life — I find it so much easier to express myself when I use social media. Another advantage is that I hardly ever forget anyone's birthday now because I can look it up online!" Lots of users agree that social media helps young people stay connected to their friends and make new friends from around the world.

However, social media also has many problems. Social media may help young people find friends, but it also makes it easier for bullies to reach their victims. Countless people have experienced bullying online, with bullies leaving nasty comments on users' profiles. Some parents also believe that social media makes it harder for families to spend time together. They say that their children are so preoccupied with social media that they ignore the rest of their family. As well as this, social media might distract pupils from their school work. Anthea Longbarrow, a teacher, said, "I find it frustrating that some pupils don't do their homework properly because they'd rather spend time on their social media accounts."

Social media definitely has some serious drawbacks, and it is very important to be mindful of spending too much time online. However, overall, social media can be a positive thing for young people. It is a way for nervous people to make friends, and for children to stay connected.

---

1. According to the text, what are *Social media websites*?

    ....

    ....

2. According to Munira, what are the positives
    of social media? Tick **two** boxes.

    It helps her remember people's birthdays.   ☐

    It helps her deal with bullying.   ☐

    It makes it harder for her to spend time with her family.   ☐

    It makes her feel more confident talking to people.   ☐

    It helps her to focus on her work.   ☐

3. *Countless people have experienced bullying online, with bullies
    leaving nasty comments on users' profiles.*
    Which word in this sentence suggests that lots of
    people have been victims of online bullying?

    ....

4. What does Anthea say is *frustrating* about social media?

....

....

5. *...it is very important to be mindful of spending too much time online.*
What does the word *mindful* mean in this sentence?

Tick **one** box.

proud ☐

wary ☐

ashamed ☐

angry ☐

6. Using your own words, summarise what
the author thinks about social media.

....

....

....

END OF TEST

/ 8

Set B: Test 6

When Pigs Fly

A medieval court. The KING sits on his throne on a raised platform, centre, surveying the room. LORDS and LADIES are seated around the perimeter. A PAGE stands below, facing him. Behind the PAGE stands JEREMY.

PAGE: Your Excellency, the final visitor today is Mr Jeremy Dumpling, representing the kingdom's pig farmers. *(To Jeremy)* You may approach His Highness.

JEREMY: *(stepping forward nervously, then kneeling)* Your Royal Highness, I have, erm... Well I have come here today to draw your attention to what may, or might, be considered as something of a national inconvenience.

KING: *(yawning)* Yes, yes, go on then. What exactly is the nature of this 'inconvenience'?

JEREMY: Well, Your Wonderfulness, it's about the pigs, you see.

KING: I had guessed as much. What exactly is the problem with these pigs?

JEREMY: Well, Your Majesty, for the past few months, very mysteriously and without warning, the pigs in the kingdom have, one by one, quite independently...

PAGE: Spit it out, man!

JEREMY: The pigs have started flying.

(The court is silent for a moment, then KING, PAGE, LORDS and LADIES erupt into raucous laughter.)

JEREMY: *(struggling to be heard over the din)* I beg your pardon, Sire, but I really am quite serious!

KING: *(catching his breath)* Pigs flying! My good man, you cannot possibly be sincere! You are quite the comedian, Mr Dumpling. Do be sure to contact my Head of Staff about joining our delightful troupe of court jesters. Until then, good day to you. Page, you may escort Mr Dumpling from the castle.

(The PAGE helps Jeremy up and starts walking him briskly away.)

JEREMY: *(wriggling free)* Sire! Sire, if you would just let me show you!

KING: *(firmly)* Young man, you are trying my patience. Shall I call my guards?

JEREMY: If you would just allow me to show you one pig, Your Joyfulness...

KING: Fine. I will permit you to show me one pig, Mr Dumpling. One pig, and one pig only.

---

1.   Which of the following is **not** present in the King's court?
      Tick **one** box.

      A page   ☐

      Jeremy   ☐

      Pigs   ☐

      Lords and ladies   ☐

      _____
      1 mark

2.   What is the *national inconvenience* that Jeremy mentions in the
      text?

      ....   _____
      1 mark

3.   Which stage direction shows the reader that the king is bored?

      ....   _____
      1 mark

4.   Why is the king *catching his breath*?

      ....

      ....   _____
      1 mark

5.   **Find** and **copy** one name that Jeremy uses to address the king.

....   _____

6.   Write the numbers 1 to 5 in the boxes to put these events from the
      script into the right order. The first one has been done for you.

Jeremy tells the king that the pigs are flying.   ☐

The page introduces Jeremy to the king.   1

The king suggests that Jeremy joins the court jesters.   ☐

The page starts to escort Jeremy out of the room.   ☐

Jeremy kneels in front of the king.   ☐

7.   What do you think might happen next in the play?
      Mention **two** things.

....

....

....

....   _____

END OF TEST

/ 8

This puzzle is a brilliant way to practise your reading skills.

Knight's News

Louisa the dragon received a letter from her friend,
Sir Jiahao the Brave. Unfortunately, she accidentally burned
some holes in the letter before she had time to read it. Write
the missing letters in the holes so that the message is complete.
One letter can fit in each hole. Then, rearrange the letters in the
dark holes to spell out the answer to the knight's riddle below.

Dear Lo◌◌sa,

I'm ◌orry that the o◌her ◌nights have bee◌ trying to
cat◌◌ you. I have tr◌◌d to ex◌lai◌ that ◌ou
are a ◌in◌ dra◌on but they do◌'t ◌elie◌e me.
I t◌ink they wo◌◌d un◌ers◌and if they got to
◌no◌ you. Ple◌◌e c◌◌e to my party at the
◌astle next We◌◌esday. The kni◌hts will be
◌◌ere and I ◌◌pe you will ◌ll make ◌riends.

Lo◌e, Jiahao

The more you take, the more
you leave behind. What am I?

ANSWER: _ _ _ _ _ _ _ _ _

You've finished a full set of tests — well done!

Now it's time to put your scores in here
and see how you're getting on.

	Score	
Test 1		/8
Test 2		/8
Test 3		/8
Test 4		/8
Test 5		/8
Test 6		/8
Total		**/48**

Once you've got a score out of 48, check it out in the table below...

0 – 23	If you got a lot of questions wrong, don't worry. Ask an adult to help you work out the **areas** you need **more practice** on. Then have another go at **this** set of tests.
24 – 36	If you got half-marks or better, you're doing well. **Read** back over your **incorrect** answers and make sure you know **why** they're wrong. Then try the **next set** of tests.
37 – 48	Woohoo! Now have a go at the **next set** of tests — can you beat your score?

But before you do... bend your brain round this one:

My first is in SPEED but never in DEEP,   My third is in DONOR but never in DOOR,
My second's in TUNA and also in CHEAP,   My fourth is in RECORD but never in CORE.

What am I? __ __ __ __

There are **5 questions** in this test.
Give yourself **10 minutes** to read the text and answer the questions.

The Lion and the Hare

There was once a brave young lion. He was strong and swift. His coat shone in the sunlight and his mane glinted like a crown around his head. When he roared, all the other animals trembled. He strutted around the plains, king of all he saw.

One afternoon, the lion awoke with a stomach as empty as a cave. There were usually many animals around for him to hunt and eat. Herds of zebras, gazelles and antelopes often grazed nearby. Wildebeests and impalas would wander through. Today was different. Today, the plains seemed empty.

For months now, there had been no rain. The waterholes where animals had gathered to drink had all dried up. Most of the animals had moved north, where the grass was greener and there was more rain.

Suddenly, from out of the corner of his eye, the lion saw the grass twitching. He turned and saw the tips of two long, brown ears. A hare, he thought. How perfect! An easy meal if ever there was one. Small, maybe, but enough for today.

The lion licked his lips and started to move towards the hare... then he stopped. He had spotted an antelope, grazing in the afternoon sunshine. The hare would make an easy meal, but if he could catch an antelope, he would have a feast!

His mouth watering, the lion made his decision. Quick as a flash, he leapt out from his hiding place and chased after the antelope. But the lion, weak and tired from lack of food, was soon left far behind.

Slowly, he turned and wandered back to the spot where he had watched the hare nibbling the grass. It was nowhere to be found.

The lion was left with nothing. Just a very empty stomach, and the feeling that maybe he should have been content with what he had to start with.

1.   What time of day is it when the story takes place?

   ....   ———
   1 mark

2.   Give **two** reasons from the text why most of the other animals in the story had gone north.

   1) ....

   2) ....   ———
   2 marks

3.   What does the word *content* mean in the final line of the text?

   ....   ———
   1 mark

4.   What is the main message of this text? Tick **one** box.

   Don't be greedy, or you might end up with nothing.   ☐

   Lions are not as smart as people think they are.   ☐

   Lions should move north with other animals.   ☐

   Never chase an antelope instead of a hare.   ☐
   ———
   1 mark

5. At the beginning of the story, why do you think that the lion is described as being the *king of all he saw*?

    Mention **two** reasons, using evidence from the rest of the story to explain your answer.

    ....

    ....

    ....

    ....

    ....

    ....

    ....
                                                                        _____
                                                                        3 marks

END OF TEST

/ 8

There are **6 questions** in this test.
Give yourself **10 minutes** to read the text and answer the questions.

Come to Chester...

The historic city of Chester is the perfect place for a weekend break, with something for the whole family to enjoy.

Roman Ruins

The city is perhaps most famous for its Roman ruins. The Romans settled in Chester almost two thousand years ago and evidence of this can still be seen today. You can walk along the impressive city walls, as the soldiers once did to watch for invaders, and appreciate the stunning views of the city.

You can find out more about the Roman settlement by visiting the Dewa Roman Experience, where lunch is complimentary. You and the kids can see and smell what a street might have been like, and even try on some armour. You can also visit the famous amphitheatre, where Roman soldiers once fought and trained.

Historic City Centre

The Rows

Chester is home to the Victorian-made Eastgate clock, arguably the second most photographed clock in the world (after Big Ben in London). A short detour from there will take you to the Rows. These timber-frame medieval buildings are unique to Chester and house a huge range of shops, from high street stores to exclusive boutiques. When you're ready to relax, take a stroll around the beautiful medieval cathedral, or stop for a picnic in Grosvenor Park.

Great Sports Facilities

If you fancy something energetic, the Northgate Arena has superb facilities, including several swimming pools (with water slides) and a spacious gym.

Fantastic Restaurants

At the end of a fun-filled day, why not enjoy a meal at one of Chester's many restaurants? There's food for all tastes and ages, from traditional pub fare to exotic Thai curries. You'll be spoilt for choice!

1. According to the text, what is Chester most well-known for?

.... ———

2. Give **one** example of a way to experience Roman life in Chester.

.... ———

3. ... *where lunch is complimentary.*
   What does the word *complimentary* mean in this sentence?

Tick **one** box.

kind ☐

complete ☐

free ☐

delicious ☐

———

4. Look at the section titled *Great Sports Facilities*.
   Find and **copy** one word or phrase from this section which makes the sports facilities in Chester sound appealing.

.... ———

5. Read each statement and **tick** to show whether it is fact or opinion.

	Fact	Opinion
The city walls in Chester are impressive.	☐	☐
You can eat Thai curry in Chester.	☐	☐
The Eastgate clock can be found in Chester.	☐	☐
There is a beautiful cathedral in Chester.	☐	☐

1 mark

6. How does the text encourage parents to visit Chester?

Mention **two** things, using evidence from the text to explain your answer.

....

....

....

....

....

....

3 marks

END OF TEST

/ 8

There are **6 questions** in this test.
Give yourself **10 minutes** to read the text and answer the questions.

For hundreds of years, it was almost always men who voted in elections in Britain. In fact, a law was even passed in 1832 that prevented any woman from being able to vote. However, towards the end of the 19th century, some people started campaigning for women to be given the right to vote.

Votes for Women

In 1897, a woman called Millicent Fawcett took charge of a group which campaigned for British women to be able to vote. Within a few years, her group had thousands of members across the country. Millicent believed in campaigning peacefully — she published books on women's rights and tried to persuade the government to change the voting laws.

Over the years, some women became frustrated by the lack of progress and they believed violent methods would be more effective. Some of these women, including Emmeline Pankhurst, were sent to prison. From 1908, Pankhurst was arrested several times for smashing windows, hitting a policeman and taking responsibility for a bomb explosion. Pankhurst, and many women like her, thought that violence was justified if it meant that women would eventually be able to vote.

Some women even died for the cause. Emily Davison was campaigning for women's votes at a horse race at Epsom in 1913. She ran out in front of the king's horse during a race and was hit. Her injuries caused her to die four days later.

The first big breakthrough was made in 1918, when some women over the age of 30 were allowed to vote. The election in 1918 was an important moment, but the campaign for women to be able to vote was not over. All men over the age of 21 could vote, so women still didn't have equal rights to men.

It wasn't until 1928 that all women over the age of 21 got the right to vote. Many women had fought courageously for years to have the same voting rights as men, and they were finally rewarded for their efforts.

---

1.   Look at the first paragraph of the text, beginning *In 1897...*
      Which phrase in this paragraph suggests
      Millicent Fawcett's group was popular?

      .... _____
                                                                                                    1 mark

2.   What does the word *frustrated* mean in paragraph two?

      .... _____
                                                                                                    1 mark

3.   How were Emmeline Pankhurst's methods
      different from Millicent Fawcett's methods.

      .... _____
                                                                                                    1 mark

4.   Draw a line to match each date to the event.

1897		Some women over the age of 30 get to vote in elections.
1908		All women over the age of 21 get to vote in elections.
1913		Millicent Fawcett becomes leader of a group who campaign for women to vote.
1918		Emily Davison dies after being injured at a horse race in Epsom.
1928		Emmeline Pankhurst is arrested for the first time.

                                                                                                    _____
                                                                                                    1 mark

5. What does the text make the reader think about the campaign to let women vote?

....

....

6. How do you think Millicent Fawcett might have felt in 1897, 1918 and 1928?

....

....

....

....

....

....

....

END OF TEST

/ 8

There are **6 questions** in this test.
Give yourself **10 minutes** to read the text and answer the questions.

The Beast Below

Under the busy city street,
Under the hustling, bustling feet,
Beneath the river and the park,
In the daylight, in the dark,
Below the city, in the tunnels deep   5
A metal dragon lies asleep.
With lightning speed and clashing claws,
From hidden lair come thunderous roars.
It waits and starts its new attack,
Slides and glides along the track.   10
With painted body, bright eyes of light
See deep into the inky night.
It snakes afar by night and day
To stations that are far away.
At every stop it opens wide   15
To rid itself of those inside.
Then idles, waiting for some more
To squeeze themselves within the door.
At times, alone, it rattles by
With hissing breath and piercing cry,   20
It sweeps along on metal rails,
With whispering sigh of twisting trails,
Under the busy city street,
Under the hustling, bustling feet,
Searching down the endless lanes   25
For those who like to ride in trains.

1. Circle the correct option to complete each sentence below.

The train is...

in a tunnel.   in a park.   on a city street.

It travels...

long distances.   short distances.   nowhere.

2 marks

---

2. *bright eyes of light* (line 11)
Which part of the train do these words describe?

....

1 mark

---

3. Draw lines to match the quotes from the text to the events they are describing.

Quotes	Events
it opens wide (line 15)	an empty train travelling along
idles, waiting (line 17)	the train doors opening
alone, it rattles by (line 19)	the train standing at a platform

1 mark

---

4.   **Find** and **copy** a word or phrase which tells you that the train can be noisy.

....   _____
                                                                                                            1 mark

5.   Towards the end of the poem, how does the writer link back to the beginning of the poem?

....

....   _____
                                                                                                            1 mark

6.   The train is described as a *dragon* (line 6).
     Explain how the description of the train in the rest of the poem supports this idea. Mention **two** things.

....

....

....

....   _____
                                                                                                            2 marks

END OF TEST

/ 8

There are **6 questions** in this test.
Give yourself **10 minutes** to read the text and answer the questions.

How Camels Survive in the Desert

The world's deserts are some of the harshest environments on the planet. Temperatures can reach over 40°C in the day, there are few water sources and little food, and there can be violent sandstorms. Camels have had to develop special characteristics to survive in these challenging conditions.

Perhaps the camel's most famous feature is its hump. This is actually a very important adaptation. If the camel cannot find any food in the desert, it can live off the fat stored in its hump instead.

Desert plants are good sources of water and nutrients for camels, but they are often spiky to try to prevent animals from eating them. In response, camels have developed thick lips and a leathery mouth so that they can eat the plants without feeling pain.

Sand is everywhere in the desert. It can be blown fiercely by the winds, so camels have to be specially adapted to cope with this. To help them keep sand out of their bodies, camels have very long eye lashes and lots of ear hairs to catch the grains. They also have the ability to close their nostril slits against the raging sands.

Because the desert is a very dry environment, with few available water sources, its inhabitants need to be efficient with their water management. Camels have very few sweat glands, allowing them to sweat less, retain the water they do consume and stay hydrated.

Despite the high temperatures, lack of food and water, and other challenges in the desert, camels are so well adapted that they are found in deserts across Africa, Asia and Australia. In fact, they have become essential for humans living in these locations, who use camels to transport food, water (and themselves) across the challenging terrains.

1. What is a camel's hump made of?

.... _____

1 mark

2. The text says that sand *can be blown fiercely by the winds.*
   What does the word *fiercely* tell you about the winds in the desert?

.... _____

1 mark

3. What does the word *retain* mean in the fifth paragraph of the text?

.... _____

1 mark

4. Where in the world can camels be found?
   Circle **one** option.

Africa, America and Asia	**Asia, Australia and Africa**
Africa, Europe and Australia	**Europe, Africa and India**

   _____

1 mark

5. How does the conclusion of the text link back to the introduction?

....

....
                                                                                    —————
1 mark

6. Using your own words, summarise **three** ways in which camels are adapted to their environment.

....

....

....

....

....

....

....
                                                                                    —————
3 marks

END OF TEST

/ 8

There are **6 questions** in this test.
Give yourself **10 minutes** to read the text and answer the questions.

An extract from 'The Swiss Family Robinson', by Johann David Wyss

The narrator, William Robinson, and his family are passengers on a ship caught in a terrible storm. The narrator is on deck; his family shelter below.

Forgetting the passengers, the ship's company crowded into the lifeboats, and the last who entered cut the davit ropes to cast each boat into the sea.

What was my horror when through the foam and spray I beheld the last remaining boat leave the ship, the last of the seamen spring into her and push off, regardless of my cries and entreaties that we might be allowed to share their slender chance of preserving their lives. My voice was drowned in the howling of the blast, and even had the crew wished it, the return of the boat was impossible, for the waves were mountain-high.

Casting my eyes despairingly around, I became gradually aware that our position was by no means hopeless, inasmuch as the stern of the ship containing our cabin was jammed between two high rocks, and was partly raised from among the breakers which dashed the fore-part to pieces. As the clouds of mist and rain drove past, I could make out, through rents in the vaporous curtain, a line of rocky coast, and, rugged as it was, my heart bounded towards it as a sign of help in the hour of need.

Yet the sense of our lonely and forsaken condition weighed heavily upon me as I returned to my family, constraining myself to say with a smile, "Courage, dear ones! Although our good ship will never sail more, she is so placed that our cabin will remain above water, and tomorrow, if the wind and waves abate, I see no reason why we should not be able to get ashore."

These few words had an immediate effect on the spirits of my children, for my family had the habit of trusting in my assurances. The boys at once regarded our problematical chance of escaping as a happy certainty, and began to enjoy the relief from the violent pitching and rolling of the vessel.

---

1. Read each statement and **tick** whether it is true or false.

	True	False
The first person in the lifeboat cut the ropes.	☐	☐
The narrator doesn't have any sons.	☐	☐
The family's cabin was in the stern of the ship.	☐	☐
The storm didn't damage the ship.	☐	☐

_____

1 mark

2. Write the numbers 1 to 5 in the boxes to put these events from the text into the right order. The first one has been done for you.

The narrator reassures his family of survival.	☐
The narrator sees the final sailors abandoning ship.	1
The narrator catches a glimpse of land.	☐
The narrator realises that they are stuck on the rocks.	☐
The narrator's family become more hopeful.	☐

_____

1 mark

3. Look at the second paragraph of the text. Why don't the sailors go back when the narrator calls out to them? Give **two** reasons.

1) ....

2) .... _____

2 marks

4. Circle **one** word that best describes the waves.

heavy   misty   tall   rugged

1 mark

5. Look at the fourth paragraph of the text, beginning *Yet the sense...*
Which phrase in this paragraph suggests that the narrator is in a terrible situation?

....

....

1 mark

6. What do you think might happen next in the text?
Mention **two** things.

....

....

....

....

2 marks

END OF TEST

/ 8

This puzzle is a brilliant way to practise your vocabulary skills.

All's Wool that Ends Wool

Liz is trying to gather up her sheep for shearing, but five of the sheep have hidden in different barns around the farm. Use the clues below to work out which sheep is hiding in which barn. Write each name under the correct barn.

Woolly
I'll tell you which barn
To look around,
It's the one whose name
Means falling down.

Barbara
The barn where you'll
Find your ewe
Is the one named with
An antonym of new.

Barnaby
It wouldn't be
A wild sheep chase
If you search in the barn
That has lots of space.

Lambert
"This barn is awful!"
I exclaim —
an antonym of fragrant
is its name.

Ramsey
It's not hard to guess
Where you'll find me —
I'm living a life of luxury.

ancient

dilapidated

sumptuous

putrid

vast

End of Set C: Scoresheet

You've finished a full set of tests — well done!

Now it's time to put your scores in here
and see how you're getting on.

	Score	
Test 1		/8
Test 2		/8
Test 3		/8
Test 4		/8
Test 5		/8
Test 6		/8
Total		**/48**

Once you've got a score out of 48, check it out in the table below...

0 – 23	If you got a lot of questions wrong, don't worry. Ask an adult to help you work out the **areas** you need **more practice** on. Then have another go at **this** set of tests.
24 – 36	If you got half-marks or better, you're doing well. **Read** back over your **incorrect** answers and make sure you know **why** they're wrong.
37 – 48	Woohoo! You've done really well — congratulations!

One last thing... bend your brain round this one:

Which word can be put after all three of these words to make three new words?

rain   water   night   The word is _____

Answers

Each question covers a reading element from the KS2 SATs.
These elements are indicated in brackets next to each answer.

Set A

Test 1 – Pages 2-4

1. (**1 mark for one correct, 2 marks for both correct**)
   1) It was hot.
   2) It was boring. (2b)

2. (**1 mark**)
   She didn't want Isha to get wet. (2b)

3. (**1 mark**) strolled (2a)

4. (**1 mark for any simple answer**)
   e.g. It tells you Isha was feeling nervous.
   (2g)

5. (**1 mark for choosing an answer and supporting the choice with a simple statement**)
   e.g. "I don't think Isha had been to that park before because she felt 'lost'." (2d)

   (**2 marks for making two points to support the choice**)
   e.g. "I don't think Isha had been to that park before because she felt 'lost' and didn't recognise any of the buildings nearby." (2d)

   (**3 marks for making three points to support the choice**)
   e.g. "I don't think Isha had been to that park before because she felt 'lost', didn't recognise any of the buildings nearby, and didn't know her way back home." (2d)

Test 2 – Pages 5-7

1. (**1 mark**)
   That you can split white light into seven different colours (2b)

2. (**1 mark for a sensible answer**)
   e.g. The reader knows what a rainbow looks like, so it helps them to picture the spectrum.
   (2d)

3. (**1 mark**)
   Make a hole in the middle, then put a pencil in the hole. 4
   Split it into seven sections. 2
   Colour in and cut out the circle. 3
   Draw a circle. 1
   Spin the disc on the table. 5 (2f)

4. (**1 mark for any three of the following**)
   a pair of compasses, (a piece of) white card, a protractor, crayons, scissors (2b)

5. (**1 mark for one of the following, or 2 marks for two of the following**)
   It calls the instructions "simple".
   It says you can do the test at home or at school.
   It says that you can use any thickness of card. (2d)

6. (**1 mark for two correct, 2 marks for all correct**)

How wide does each section of the circle need to be?	(about) 51 degrees (wide)
What should the diameter of the circle be?	10 centimetres (or cm)
Which two colours should be next to blue on the circle?	indigo and green

   (2b)

Test 3 – Pages 8-10

1. (**1 mark for both correct**)
   1) the person's ankles
   2) the structure they're jumping off (2b)

2. (**1 mark**)
   Because this is where commercial bungee jumping first began. (2b)

3. (**1 mark**) Zambia. (2b)

Answers

4. (**1 mark for both correct**)
   1) thrill
   2) spectacular
   (2g)

5. (**1 mark for all correct**)
   People bungee jump from cranes.
   — Fact
   The Verzasca Dam is one of the highest permanent jumping sites in the world. — Fact
   Bungee jumping is thrilling. — Opinion (2d)

6. (**1 mark for suggesting feelings with one piece of supporting evidence**)
   e.g. "They might feel nervous because bungee jumping is a 'dangerous' sport." (2d)

   (**2 marks for suggesting feelings with two pieces of supporting evidence**)
   e.g. "They might feel nervous because bungee jumping is a 'dangerous' sport, and people have died when jumping." (2d)

   (**3 marks for suggesting feelings with three pieces of supporting evidence**)
   e.g. "They might feel nervous because bungee jumping is a 'dangerous' sport, and people have died when jumping. However, they might also feel excited because it's a 'thrilling' experience." (2d)

Test 4 – Pages 11-13

1. (**1 mark**) September (2b)

2. (**1 mark for any simple answer**)
   e.g. He feels very angry. (2a)

3. (**1 mark for any sensible comparison**)
   e.g. In captivity an elephant has little space but in the wild they have lots of space. (2h)

4. (**1 mark**) Africa (2b)

5. (**1 mark**) Leave Nia in Africa. (2c)

6. (**1 mark for suggesting how Mr Clarke would feel with one piece of supporting evidence**)
   e.g. "Mr Clarke would not approve of elephants being used in the circus because he thinks that captivity is 'a crime'." (2d)

   (**2 marks for suggesting how Mr Clarke would feel with two pieces of supporting evidence**)
   e.g. "Mr Clarke would not approve of elephants being used in the circus because he thinks that captivity is 'a crime'. Like the zoo, the circus would also be keeping the elephants 'prisoner'." (2d)

   (**3 marks for suggesting how Mr Clarke would feel with three pieces of supporting evidence**)
   e.g. "Mr Clarke would not approve of elephants being used in the circus because he thinks that captivity is 'a crime'. Like the zoo, the circus would be keeping the elephants 'prisoner'. Mr Clarke didn't like the idea that people would 'gawp' at the elephants in the zoo, and this would be the same in the circus." (2d)

Test 5 – Pages 14-16

1. (**1 mark for both correct**)
   1) the sky
   2) the sea (2d)

2. (**1 mark**) a bird (2b)

3. (**1 mark**) At sea (2b)

4. (**1 mark**) Conflict (2a)

5. (**1 mark**) fifty (2b)

6. (**1 mark for two points with no supporting evidence**)
   e.g. "The sea plays and the sea can speak." (2c)

   (**1 mark for one point with supporting evidence**)
   e.g. "The poet describes the sea like a child, for example, 'It plays with the clouds'." (2c)

(**1 mark for one piece of evidence, without a point**)
e.g. "It plays with the clouds". (2c)

(**2 marks for two points, with one piece of supporting evidence**)
e.g. "The poet uses describes the sea like a child, for example, 'It plays with the clouds'. The sea can also speak." (2c)

(**3 marks for two points, each with a piece of supporting evidence**)
e.g. "The poet describes the sea like a child, for example, 'It plays with the clouds'. The poet also says the sea makes noises like a human: it "whistles" and "tells". (2c)

Test 6 – Pages 17-19

1. (**1 mark**) Cylinder (2b)

2. (**1 mark**) paralysed (2a)

3. (**1 mark**) evening (2d)

4. (**1 mark for any of the following**)
'continually looking at the sand heaps'
'What could be going on there?'
'a passionate longing to peer into it.' (2g)

5. (**1 mark for any sensible answer**)
e.g. noticed (2a)

6. (**1 mark for all correct**)
The narrator speaks to his neighbour. ☐3
A rod rises up out of the spacecraft. ☐2
The neighbour is seen heading towards Woking. ☐5
The narrator sees the Martians emerge. ☐1
The narrator climbs a small hill to get a better view. ☐4 (2f)

7. (**1 mark for one piece of supporting evidence**)
e.g. "People have gathered around the pit to see what's happening." (2d)

(**2 marks for two pieces of supporting evidence**)
e.g. "People have gathered around the pit to see what's happening. The narrator has a feeling of 'fascination' at the crash landing." (2d)

Puzzle – Page 20

The words are: p**etrif**y, sp**oo**k, **fright**en, al**arm**, un**nerve**, **st**artle, sh**ock**, **scare**, inti**mida**te.

The scariest thing in the house is a **spider**.

Scoresheet Question – Page 21

giving, toilet, parsnip, bathtub

Set B

Test 1 – Pages 22-24

1. (**1 mark**)
the ultimate summer adventure (2b)

2. (**1 mark**) array (2a)

3. (**1 mark for either of the following**)
a fortnight OR two weeks (2b)

4. (**1 mark**) campfires (2b)

5. (**1 mark for all correct**)
You might be in the Kingfishers team at Fierce Forest. — False
Fierce Forest is suitable for 11-year-olds. — True
Everyone gets to go treetop exploring. — False
There are four different activities to choose from. — False (2d)

6. (**1 mark for two points (one for each audience) with no evidence**)
e.g. "The camp sounds like a game that children want to take part in. The text also makes parents feel that their children would be safe." (2d)

Answers

(**1 mark for one point with supporting evidence**)
e.g. "The text mentions an 'amazing array of activities' making the camp seem fun-filled to children." (2d)

(**1 mark for one piece of evidence, without a point**)
e.g. "space to just kick back and relax" (2d)

(**2 marks for two points (one for each audience) with one piece of evidence**)
e.g. "The fact that you can get prizes makes the camp sound exciting for children. The parents would trust the leaders." (2d)

(**3 marks for two points (one for each audience), both with supporting evidence**)
e.g. "Being taught the 'ways of the wild' sounds exciting to children. The camp leaders are described as 'experts' so parents would trust them to care for the children." (2d)

Test 2 – Pages 25-27

1. (**1 mark**) Her grandfather (2b)

2. (**1 mark for all correct**)
Ella's grandfather makes the best casserole.
— Opinion
Ella has always lived in Norwich.
— Fact
Being a chef is always stressful. — Opinion
(2d)

3. (**1 mark for any sensible answer**)
e.g. Preparing food for customers at the restaurant. (2b)

4. (**1 mark for both correct**)
1) how stressful the job can be
2) the long hours (2b)

5. (**1 mark for any sensible answer**)
e.g. "You need to work hard." (2d)

6. (**1 mark for making a simple comment on what Ella might do**)
e.g. Ella might help the person with their cooking. (2d)

(**2 marks for saying what Ella might do, with one piece of supporting evidence**)
e.g. Ella might help the person with their cooking because this is what her grandfather did to encourage her. (2d)

(**3 marks for saying what Ella might do, with two pieces of supporting evidence**)
e.g. Ella might help the person with their cooking because this is what her grandfather did to encourage her. She might also encourage them to try new recipes to show them that cooking can be interesting. (2d)

Test 3 – Pages 28-30

1. (**1 mark**) build a labyrinth. (2b)

2. (**1 mark for any sensible answer**)
e.g. Because he wanted to go back to Greece. OR Because the King wouldn't let him leave. (2d)

3. (**1 mark for any sensible answer**)
e.g. The birds were very agile.
OR The birds moved gracefully. (2g)

4. (**1 mark for any sensible answer**)
e.g. that he is amazed by them OR he thinks they are interesting OR he can't stop looking at them (2a)

5. (**1 mark for any sensible answer**)
e.g. Because he didn't want the King to find out. (2d)

6. (**1 mark for making a simple comment**)
e.g. "Icarus flies too close to the sun." (2c)

(**2 marks for an answer which mentions two events in order**)
e.g. "Daedalus and Icarus fly towards Greece, but then Icarus flies so high that his wings melt." (2c)

(**3 marks for an answer which mentions at least three events in order**)
e.g. "Daedalus and Icarus put their wings on, and Daedalus warns his son not to fly too close to the sun otherwise the wings will melt. Then they take off, but Icarus does fly

Answers

too close to the sun, so he falls into the sea and drowns." (2c)

Test 4 – Pages 31-33

1. (**1 mark for all correct**)
   The Fun Day began at 9am. — False
   The 'Soak a Teacher' event was at 4pm. — True
   Sophia's mother is Mary Martin. — False
   The Fun Day raised £1000 in total. — False (2b)

2. (**1 mark**) April (2b)

3. (**1 mark**) Because he has taken part in the 'Soak a Teacher' event. (2d)

4. (**1 mark for either of the following**)
   Once a fortnight. OR
   Once every two weeks. (2b)

5. (**1 mark**) Basketball (2b)

6. (**1 mark for any sensible answer**)
   e.g. The support is very important. OR You can't put a price on the support it provides. OR The support makes a big difference to the Martin family. (2a)

7. (**1 mark for a sensible answer without a reason**)
   e.g. "She feels very happy."
   OR "She is grateful." (2d)

   (**2 marks for a sensible answer with supporting evidence**)
   e.g. "She feels grateful because she enjoys going to St. Mary's Hospital." (2d)

Test 5 – Pages 34-36

1. (**1 mark**)
   online communities where people can share photos and talk to each other (2b)

2. (**1 mark for one correct, 2 marks for both correct**)
   It helps her remember people's birthdays.
   It makes her feel more confident talking to people. (2b)

3. (**1 mark**) Countless (2a)

4. (**1 mark**) It stops children from doing their homework properly. (2b)

5. (**1 mark**) wary (2a)

6. (**1 mark for a simple comment**)
   e.g. "The reporter thinks social media is good." (2c)

   (**2 marks for an answer that covers the conclusion and the drawbacks**)
   e.g. "The reporter thinks social media is good, but that children should be aware of its drawbacks." (2c)

Test 6 – Pages 37-39

1. (**1 mark**) Pigs (2b)

2. (**1 mark for any sensible answer**)
   e.g. The pigs have started flying. OR The pigs in the kingdom are flying away. (2b)

3. (**1 mark**) 'yawning' (2d)

4. (**1 mark**)
   Because he has been laughing. (2d)

5. (**1 mark for any of the following**)
   'Your Royal Highness'
   'Your Wonderfulness'
   'Your Majesty'
   'Sire'
   'Your Joyfulness' (2b)

6. (**1 mark for all correct**)
   Jeremy tells the king that the pigs are flying. ③
   The page introduces Jeremy to the king. ①
   The king suggests that Jeremy joins the court jesters. ④
   The page starts to escort Jeremy out of the room. ⑤
   Jeremy kneels in front of the king. ② (2f)

7. (**1 mark for a sensible answer which mentions one event**)
   e.g. "Jeremy will bring a pig into the room." (2e)

Answers

(2 marks for a sensible answer which mentions two events)
e.g. "Jeremy will bring a flying pig into the room and the king will faint in shock." (2e)

Puzzle – Page 40

Dear Louisa,

I'm sorry that the other knights have been trying to catch you. I have tried to explain that you are a kind dragon but they don't believe me. I think they would understand if they got to know you. Please come to my party at the castle next Wednesday. The knights will be there and I hope you will all make friends.

Love, Jiahao

Answer: footsteps

Scoresheet Question – Page 41

SAND

Set C

Test 1 – Pages 42-44

1. **(1 mark)** afternoon (2b)

2. **(1 mark for one of the following, or 2 marks for two of the following)**
    there had been no rain for months
    the waterholes had dried up
    the grass was greener in the north
    there was more rain in the north (2b)

3. **(1 mark for any sensible answer)**
    e.g. pleased OR satisfied OR happy (2a)

4. **(1 mark)**
    Don't be greedy, or you might end up with nothing. (2c)

5. **(1 mark for two points with no supporting evidence)**
    e.g. "He looks like a king, and he's very powerful." (2d)

(1 mark for one point with supporting evidence)
e.g. "The lion is very powerful like a king — he's described as 'strong and swift'." (2d)

(1 mark for one piece of evidence, without a point)
e.g. "strong and swift" (2d)

(2 marks for two points, with one piece of supporting evidence)
e.g. "The other animals 'trembled' when the lion roared, which suggests he is more powerful than them. He looks like a king, too." (2d)

(3 marks for two points, each with a piece of supporting evidence)
e.g. "The other animals 'trembled' when the lion roared, which suggests he is more powerful than them. He looks like a king, because his mane looks like a crown." (2d)

Test 2 – Pages 45-47

1. **(1 mark)** Roman ruins (2b)

2. **(1 mark for any of the following)**
    walk along the city walls
    visit the Dewa Roman Experience
    see what a street might have been like
    try on armour
    visit the amphitheatre (2b)

3. **(1 mark)** free (2a)

4. **(1 mark for either of the following)**
    'superb (facilities)' OR 'spacious (gym)' (2g)

5. **(1 mark for all correct)**
    The city walls in Chester are impressive. — Opinion
    You can eat Thai curry in Chester. — Fact
    The Eastgate clock can be found in Chester. — Fact
    There is a beautiful cathedral in Chester. — Opinion (2d)

6. **(1 mark for two points with no supporting evidence)**
    e.g. "The whole family can have fun and can eat there." (2d)

Answers

(1 mark for one point with supporting evidence)
e.g. "The introduction says that 'the whole family' will enjoy a visit to Chester." (2d)

(1 mark for one piece of evidence, without a point)
e.g. "something for the whole family to enjoy" (2d)

(2 marks for two points, with one piece of supporting evidence)
e.g. "The text makes it seem like children are welcome by mentioning 'the kids'. Everyone can eat there, too." (2d)

(3 marks for two points, each with a piece of supporting evidence)
e.g. "The introduction says that the 'whole family' will enjoy a visit to Chester, and at the end of the text it says that there is food for 'all' ages, so parents would be keen to bring their children." (2d)

Test 3 – Pages 48-50

1. **(1 mark)** 'thousands of members (across the country)' (2g)

2. **(1 mark for any sensible answer)**
e.g. annoyed OR discouraged (2a)

3. **(1 mark)** Pankhurst's methods were more violent than Fawcett's. (2h)

4. **(1 mark for all correct)**

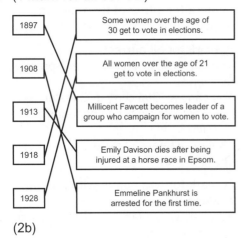

(2b)

5. **(1 mark for any sensible answer)**
e.g. The reader thinks that the campaign was a good thing that took a lot of courage. (2d)

6. **(1 mark for a simple answer about one point in time)**
e.g. "She probably felt pleased when women were allowed to vote in 1928." (2e)

(2 marks for an answer that mentions two different points in time)
e.g. "She felt angry that women couldn't vote in 1897 when she started campaigning, but happy when women were allowed to vote in 1928." (2e)

(3 marks for an answer that mentions all three points in time)
e.g. "She felt angry that women couldn't vote in 1897 when she started campaigning, but might have felt a bit better when women over 30 years old were allowed to vote in 1918. She probably felt really happy when all women over 21 years old could vote in 1928." (2e)

Test 4 – Pages 51-53

1. **(1 mark for one correct, 2 marks for both correct)**
in a tunnel.
long distances. (2b)

2. **(1 mark)** the headlights (2d)

3. **(1 mark for all correct)**

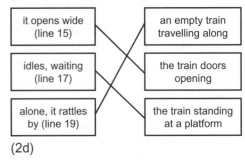

(2d)

4. **(1 mark for either of the following)**
'thunderous (roars)' OR 'piercing (cry)' (2d)

Answers

5. (**1 mark for any sensible answer**)
e.g. The writer repeats the first two lines of the poem. (2f)

6. (**1 mark for one sensible answer, 2 marks for two sensible answers**)
e.g. The sounds it makes sound like the sounds a dragon would make.
Its movements are fast and smooth like a dragon's might be. (2d)

Test 5 – Pages 54-56

1. (**1 mark**) fat (2b)

2. (**1 mark for any sensible answer**)
e.g. that the winds are strong OR that the winds are powerful (2a)

3. (**1 mark for any sensible answer**)
e.g. keep OR hold OR store (2a)

4. (**1 mark**) Asia, Australia and Africa (2b)

5. (**1 mark for any sensible answer**)
e.g. They both mention the conditions in the desert. OR They both say that camels are well adapted to the desert. (2f)

6. (**1 mark for one adaptation with an explanation**)
e.g. "They have a hump which they can live off when there isn't any food." (2d)

(**2 marks for two adaptations with explanations**)
e.g. "They can close their nostrils to keep sand out of their bodies, and they don't sweat too much because there isn't much water." (2d)

(**3 marks for three adaptations with explanations**)
e.g. "Camels have long eyelashes to keep sand out of their eyes, and they have a hump of fat to live off when there isn't any food. They also have a leathery mouth so they can eat the spiky desert plants." (2d)

Test 6 – Pages 57-59

1. (**1 mark for all correct**)
The first person in the lifeboat cut the ropes. — False
The narrator doesn't have any sons. — False
The family's cabin was in the stern of the ship. — True
The storm didn't damage the ship. — False
(2b)

2. (**1 mark for all correct**)
The narrator reassures his family of survival. 4
The narrator sees the final sailors abandoning ship. 1
The narrator catches a glimpse of land. 3
The narrator realises that they are stuck on the rocks. 2
The narrator's family become more hopeful. 5 (2f)

3. (**1 mark for one sensible answer, 2 marks for two sensible answers**)
e.g. Because the storm drowns out his voice. Because the waves are too high. (2b)

4. (**1 mark**) tall (2b)

5. (**1 mark for most or all of the phrase**)
'lonely and forsaken condition' (2g)

6. (**1 mark for a sensible answer which mentions one event**)
e.g. "The storm will stop." (2e)

(**2 marks for a sensible answer which mentions two events**)
e.g. "The storm will stop and the family will manage to get to shore." (2e)

Puzzle – Page 60

Woolly — dilapidated, Barnaby — vast, Barbara — ancient, Lambert — putrid, Ramsey — sumptuous

Scoresheet Question – Page 61

fall

Progress Chart

You've finished all the tests in the book — well done!

Now it's time to put your scores in here
and see how you've done.

	Set A	Set B	Set C
Test 1			
Test 2			
Test 3			
Test 4			
Test 5			
Test 6			
Total			

See if you're on target by checking your marks for each set in the table below.

Mark	
0-23	You're not quite there yet — keep going back over the questions you find tricky and you'll improve your reading skills in no time.
24-36	Good job! You're doing really well, but make sure you keep working on your weaker topics so that you're really ready for your test.
37-48	Give yourself a huge pat on the back — you're on track to ace your test! You're a reading star — well done!

EXPR24

This page may be photocopied